Jimmy, Donkey of the Somme

CLARE LAWRENCE

ILLUSTRATED BY ANTHONY WILLIAMS

Titles in Ignite II

Badger Publishing Limited
Oldmedow Road,
Hardwick Industrial Estate,
King's Lynn PE30 4JJ
Telephone: 01438 791037

www.badgerlearning.co.uk

2 4 6 8 10 9 7 5 3 1

Jimmy, Donkey of the Somme ISBN 978-1-78147-448-8

Text © Clare Lawrence 2013
Complete work © Badger Publishing Limited 2013

Publisher: Susan Ross
Senior Editor: Danny Pearson
Publishing Assistant: Jennifer Brough
Design: Fiona Grant
Illustration: Anthony Williams
Copyeditor: Ursula Faulkner

Contents

Vocabulary:

bayonet	billeted
casualties	dugout
regiment	relieved
no man's land	salute
telegram	Veterinary Corp

Main characters:

Geordie

Jimmy

CHAPTER 1

2nd July, 1916

*Letters sent from France by Private
Geordie Watkins, aged 18.*

2nd July, 1916

Dear Mam,

We went 'over the top' this morning at
5:45am. It was still dark, misty and
very cold.

I remember the huge noise of the
barrage before we went and then the
silence.

There was complete, absolute silence broken by the officer's whistle as the sign to advance.

We overtook the first German trench line and they fell back to the line behind.

I'm not allowed to tell you any details of the fighting. I do want to tell you about the one good thing to come out of it.

Between the two lines there was just mud and bodies and rats... but I could see a German pack donkey wounded very badly in its neck and shoulder.

It was braying and struggling, but kept
trying to swing its head around to its
tail as it lay down.

McKenzie was a farm boy back home.
He said, "She's in labour, that one."
I didn't know what he meant at first,
but then I got it – she was having a foal.

I couldn't believe it! In all the death
and horror here was new life beginning.

I did a mad thing, Mam.

I'm sorry – but I had to.

I took off my tunic jacket and stuck it onto my bayonet. It wasn't white (how could anything be white out here?) but it was a flag. I waved it back and forth.

Then, very slowly, I climbed up out of the trench. Everything stopped. No one fired at me. No one even seemed to move.

I made my way through the slime and the mess to the donkey's side. She was done for... but there in the mud lay a tiny, newborn foal.

I picked him up in my arms and carried him back to the trenches.

And do you know what I heard? I heard cheering from our lads and I heard it from their lads too. Perhaps all of us in this terrible place felt we had done something good at last.

I love you, Mam. Give my love to Sissy too.

Geordie

CHAPTER 2

18th July, 1916

18th July, 1916

Dear Mam,

We are back at camp – and Jimmy is doing fine!

I didn't think we'd get him through the night.

He was freezing cold, wet and his head flopped down as I carried him.

When I got him back into the trench I gave him a gentle rub with my coat, to try to get his blood flowing.

Then I put the coat back on and tucked him inside, against the warmth of my body.

I don't know if it comforted him but it did me. I was shaking and I think I may have been crying too.

The Sarge told me to go down into the dugout. I lay there all through the night, just holding the foal.

The Sarge came down to find me at dawn.

We were supposed to 'hold the line' and I should have been up on duty. He didn't seem to mind though.

He brought McKenzie down, and a tin of milk he'd found among the German supplies.

The little donkey looked a bit stronger after his night's rest and McKenzie showed me how to feed him from my cupped hands.

The donkey suckled hard on my finger and I trickled milk down into his mouth.

McKenzie was delighted with him. "There, Our Jimmy," he said. "That'll make you stronger."

I think he just meant 'Jimmy' like I might have said 'Old Chap', but somehow the name stuck. The donkey has been 'Our Jimmy' from that moment – and a Scottish Regiment donkey by adoption!

We fell back yesterday. I carried Jimmy and some of the other lads carried my pack and rifle for me.

I won't tell you of the terrible sights as we travelled back through the bit of land we had just fought for. I held tight to Jimmy, all the way.

Love to you all.

Geordie

CHAPTER 3

16th January, 1917

Telegram: To Watkins, 23 Ellis Street, Dumfries.

'Regret to inform you Pvt G P Watkins, The 1st Battalion, Cameronian (Scottish Rifles) Regiment wounded November 3rd...'

16th January, 1917

Dear Mam,

Thanks for your last letter and parcel, which caught up with me soon after I got back.

I can't tell you how wonderful it was to see you both last month!

I can't say it's good to be back in France but I do have one piece of good news for you – Jimmy is looking fine!

I rejoined the regiment just as they were being moved back up the line.

Jimmy has been billeted at a farm, a little behind the lines, and is now big and strong.

He helps carry water supplies up to the front lines and is a real favourite with everyone. I'm sure he recognised me though!

I've put in a request to work with him as much as possible – we'll have to see what they say.

It's very cold here, but at least the mud is frozen over which makes life a little easier.

Please could you send more chocolate in your next parcel? And some dried fruit if you can – figs or apricots.
And some more socks would be great if you can manage them.

Thanks, Mam.

By the way, I'm trying to teach Jimmy to 'salute' by raising a hoof.

The lads all laugh at me but he's a clever little chap and I'll bet he'll learn...

Love for now, and to Sissy.

Geordie

CHAPTER 4

3rd May, 1917

3rd May, 1917

Dear Mam,

Thank you for your letter.

Sorry to hear about Uncle Albert, although at 93 he had a good life. It's hard to imagine 93 out here!

We are all very tired but at least I have Jimmy to keep me going.

I told you that he was wounded last month? This morning I was sent to fetch him back from the Veterinary Corp hospital and found everyone is very fond of him.

They had paired him up with a huge horse – must have been 17 hands high – as a joke on me. Very funny!

They laughed on the other side of their faces when I called him to attention and he responded with a smart salute with his hoof.

They didn't know he could do that!

The really rotten duty we have to do is collecting the dead bodies from 'no man's land'. It is grim work.

Jimmy wears a harness and pulls a stretcher. We load the bodies on to pull them back behind lines for burial.

A strange thing happened right at the end yesterday. I came across two men in a shell hole, both injured but alive.

One was a young German and the other
a Private from our lads.

I loaded them onto Jimmy's stretcher
and we took them both back to the
hospital. They were laughing together
and even shared a cigarette.

Why is it that men can get on so well
when hauled together from death,
when hours before they were trying
their best to kill each other?

My love to you both as ever.

Geordie

28th May, 1917

28th May, 1917

Dear Mam,

Just a quick note as we are moving up the line again shortly.

The weather is picking up now and at last the mud is drying. Spirits are high and everyone says the war cannot last for much longer.

You know a funny thing? The 'Private' I mentioned in my last letter, that Jimmy and I brought in from the shell hole, turned out to be an officer.
(It's not unusual for officers to swap uniforms these days – who wants to go over the top marked out as a target?)

He was so pleased with Jimmy he has put him up to be made an honorary sergeant!

If it is agreed, he will have three stripes on his head collar and be 'Sgt Jimmy of the 1st Scottish Rifles'. Then won't we be proud.

Give my love to Sissy, Mam – and to you too, of course.

Geordie

That was the last letter written by Geordie Watkins.

Later that day, a shell landed just behind him and Jimmy as they carried supplies up to the front line. Both were badly injured.

Geordie insisted that they were both loaded into the cart that took them back behind the lines, but on arrival Geordie was found to be dead.

He had died with his face buried in his friend's mane. Jimmy recovered from that wound, and from several others.

He was indeed made an honorary Sergeant.

He continued to help his friends in the regiment for the remainder of the war, carrying water and other supplies up to the front line, and the wounded back to hospital.

At the end of the war the soldiers brought him home to England with them, where he finally left the army.

He was bought at auction by Mrs Heath and spent the rest of his life raising money for the RSPCA.

He gave rides to local children in a little cart and was a famous figure in the town. The local newspaper ran a weekly column about Jimmy and the money that he raised.

Jimmy died of old age just short of his 27th birthday. He is buried in Peterborough's Central Park.

In 2003, his grave was restored and rededicated. The service was attended by a Colonel from his old regiment, a pipe band and over 2,000 people including hundreds of children.

His memorial reads:

Our Jimmy

~

Born on the Somme July 2nd 1916
Mascot of the 1st Scottish Rifles
Died May 10th 1943
Bought by Mrs Heath in 1920
To give him a good home
And to promote interest in the RSPCA

Visit him sometime, and remember Geordie – and all like him – who, like Jimmy, are now at peace.

The Battle of the Somme

Jimmy was born during the Battle of the Somme, named after the River Somme in northern France. The name of the river comes from a word meaning 'peaceful' or 'sleepy'.

The battle was one of the bloodiest in history, with over one million casualties.

Fighting took place from trenches, with the soldiers going 'over the top' to cross 'no man's land' and try to take the enemy trench ahead. In the four years of the war the same small areas of land were fought over again and again.

Food, water and ammunition was brought up to the trenches on both sides by horses, mules and donkeys.

These animals fought through the mud and rain throughout the war. Many millions died or were killed.

The Animals in War Memorial in Hyde Park, London, is a tribute to all the animals that served, suffered and died in the conflicts of the 20th century.

The RSPCA

The Royal Society for the Prevention of Cruelty to Animals is the oldest animal welfare charity in the world.

During the Great War, the RSPCA supported the work of the Veterinary Corp. through the Fund for Sick and Wounded Horses.

After his retirement to Peterborough, Jimmy was a powerful reminder of the role of animals in war. He helped to raise many thousands of pounds for the charity.

Questions

What did Geordie use as a flag?

Why were the sights 'terrible' as they fell back?

Geordie says he is 'back in France'. Where had he been?

Why was the officer Geordie saved dressed as a Private?

What do you think is the answer to the question that Geordie asks at the end of his fourth letter?